SEVEN
SMELLY SOCKS

Written by
KATE RUTTLE

Illustrated by
EMMA FOSTER

WAYLAND

First published in 2011
by Wayland

Text copyright © Kate Ruttle 2011

Illustration copyright © Wayland 2011

Wayland
338 Euston Road
London NW1 3BH

Wayland Australia
Level 17/207 Kent Street
Sydney, NSW 2000

Series editor: Louise John
Editor: Katie Woolley
Designer: Paul Cherrill
Consultant: Kate Ruttle

A CIP catalogue record for this book is available
from the British Library.

ISBN 9780750263894

Printed in China

Wayland is a division of Hachette Children's Books,
an Hachette UK company. www.hachette.co.uk

FIZZ WIZZ PHONICS is a series of fun and exciting books, especially designed to be used by children who have not yet started to read.

The books support the development of language, exploring key speaking and listening skills, as well as encouraging confidence in pre-reading skills.

SEVEN SMELLY SOCKS is all about alliteration. This is the occurrence of the same letter (grapheme) or sound (phoneme) at the beginning of closely connected words. The book uses fun tongue twisters to help to tune children's ears to the sounds that make up different words. Once children can hear and tell you what the repeated sound is in each sentence, they will soon learn to tell you the first sound in a word.

For suggestions on how to use **SEVEN SMELLY SOCKS** and for further activities, look at page 24 of this book.

Seven Smelly Socks

Suzie had seven smelly socks.

"Such smelly socks!" said Sahil.

Angry Astronaut

The ants ate Adam the astronaut's apple.

"Such annoying ants," said Adam.
"I'm an angry astronaut."

Polar Bear's Party

Panda was playing pass the parcel at Polar Bear's party.

"Pass the parcel to Penguin,"
said Parrot.

Dancing Dinosaurs

Dragon played the drums
and the dinosaurs did a dance.

"Dancing dinosaurs make me dizzy,"
said Dog.

Fantastic Fireworks

The fantastic fireworks flashed and fizzed.

"Fireworks are fabulous fun!"
said Fran.

Rocky the Rhino

Rocky the rhino rumbled
past Ravi on his red bike.

"A rhino riding a red bike?
Ridiculous!" said Ravi.

Lucky Leo

Little Leo licked his lovely
lemon lollipop.

"Lucky Leo," said Lucy.
"I love lemon lollipops!"

Gordon the Goat

Gordon the greedy goat gobbled green grass until it was gone.

"You greedy goat!" said Gavin.

Oscar and Olga

Oscar the octopus sat opposite Olga the ostrich and peeled an orange.

"Orange for Olga?" asked Oscar.

Jumping Juggler

Jon the jumping juggler juggled
with jam, jelly and a jug of juice.

"Jolly good juggling," said Jon.

Further Activities

These activities can be used when reading the book one-to-one, or in the home.

P4 • Read the sentences on this page aloud. Which sound can you hear most?
• Can you find any objects in the picture that don't begin with a 's' sound?

P6 • Read the sentences aloud and talk about the 'a' words.
• Look at the picture. Can you see what is happening in it? How can we tell that Adam is an astronaut?

P8 • Say the sentences on this page aloud and try and make the 'p' sounds stand out in each sentence.

P10 • Can you identify the repeated 'd' sound in these sentences?

P12 • Look in a mirror as you read these sentences. Make the 'f' sound long and fizzy. Can you see how you place your mouth and lips when you make the sound?
• Think of some other 'f' words and try saying them aloud while looking in the mirror, too.

P14 • Using a mirror, look at your mouth when you say the sentences on this page. Can you hear the same sound in the words you are speaking?

P16 • Can you find the 'lovely lemon lollipop' in the picture?
• Look at the word 'lollipop'. Can you see all of the 'l's in the word?
• Can you find a capital 'L' at the beginning of a name in any of the sentences on this page?

P18 • Which goat is Gordon? Talk about how you know this. Who is Gavin in the picture?
• Talk about the other animals in the picture. Which of them might also have a 'g' in their name?

P20 • Read the sentences aloud and talk about the words beginning with an 'o' sound.
• Practice writing the letter 'o' shape. Remember to begin at the top of the letter each time.

P22 • Which sound can you hear most in these sentences?
• Try reading the sentences aloud but replace Jon's juggling items with other 'j' words or objects shown in the picture.

These activities can be used when using the book with more than one child, or in an educational setting.

P4 • Can you think of any other names that begin with 's'? Perhaps someone in your group has a name beginning with 's'. Try to say the sentences again but replace Suzie or Sahil's name with another name beginning with 's'.

P6 • Do you know that names begin with capital letters? Have a look at a lower case 'a' and a capital 'A'. Can you find these letters in the sentences on this page?

P8 • Identify all of the animals in the picture: 'panda', 'penguin', 'parrot', 'monkey', 'polar bear'. Which name is different? Do you know why?

P10 • As a group, can you think of another phrase that describes what the dog is doing in this picture, for example 'Dog is dancing with dragon.'

P12 • Use the Internet to find videos of fireworks. Talk about the sounds they make.
• Can you think of other things that begin with 'f'? Try to make long, fizzy 'f's when you say these words, too.

P14 • Talk about the other things you can see in this picture that begin with 'r', for example 'rock', 'rabbit', 'rose'.
• As a group, have a go at making up new sentences using the other 'r' words you have found in the picture.

P16 • Sit down in pairs and look at your partner's face. Try and say the words 'lemon lollipop' while your partner watches to see how the shape of your mouth changes as you talk.

P18 • Look at the picture as a group and talk about all of the different things you can see in it. Try saying the sounds of some of the things in the picture, for example 'g-oa-t', 'g-r-a-ss', 'g-a-te'.

P20 • Try and make an octopus with eight legs using some sheets of paper and sticky tape. Can you think of eight objects beginning with 'o' — one for each of the octopus's legs? You could use words that have 'o' in the middle of them, for example 'cot' or 'dog', as well as at the beginning.

P22 • Try and write the beginning of the first sentence on page 22: 'Jon the jumping juggler juggled with...'
• Draw pictures of 'j' words to finish the sentence, cut them out and put them at the end of your sentence. Then read your sentence aloud to your group.